Captain Video, Elliot Ness, Ethel Mertz, Amos McCoy, Illya Kuryakin
Regis Philbin, Barney T. Fife, Alan Brady, Jay Silverheels
Pvt. Doberman, Ponce Ponce, Snooky Lanson, Rowdy Yates
Eddie Haskell, Artemus Gordon, Crazy Guggenheim
Maynard G. Krebs, Grindl, J. Fred Muggs
Della Street, Michael Anthony, Schultzy, Jane Hathaway
Mona McCluskey. . . .

If any of the above strike a responsive chord in you, then you're ready to play

THE WORLD'S GREATEST T.V. QUIZ!

All your favorite shows!
All your favorite performers!
All your favorite memories!

THE WORLD'S GREATEST T.V. QUIZ

Tom Bornhauser
and Dennis Palumbo

A BERKLEY MEDALLION BOOK
published by
BERKLEY PUBLISHING CORPORATION

To our ladies, Nancy and Judy

Published by arrangement with the authors

Berkley Publishing Corporation
200 Madison Avenue
New York, New York 10016

SBN 425-02703-1

BERKLEY MEDALLION BOOKS are published by
Berkley Publishing Corporation
200 Madison Avenue
New York, N.Y. 10016

BERKLEY MEDALLION BOOKS ® TM 757,375

Printed in the United States of America

Berkley Medallion Edition, November, 1974

TABLE OF CONTENTS

Contents

Contents

ACKNOWLEDGMENT

The authors gratefully acknowledge the co-operation, guidance, and advice of the following people, without whose assistance this book would not have been possible:

Mr. and Mrs. J. B. Tabler; William Biggs Tabler III; Pat Reilling; William Waverly Townes V; John Dorkin and William Campbell; Edward Brownstein and Dolores Sherfick; Tony Williams; Wolfgang and Mac; all the ladies who lost on *Queen for a Day;* and, of course, Mario and Dolores and Andy and Weegee.

INTRODUCTION

So you think you know all there is to know about television?

Sure, you know who starred in *The Honeymooners* and who played Pa Cartwright on *Bonanza*; you know how the castaways arrived on *Gilligan's Island* and what the Lone Ranger's bullets were made of; you know Batman's true identity and who hosted *The Twilight Zone.*

That's very nice.

But do you really know all there is to know? Or all you'd like to know?

You have in your hands the answer to your dreams.

This book is for all types of television watchers. The seasoned professional and the neophyte. The casual observer and the glutton with four TV sets in every room. The Western buff and the musical variety fan. The news hounds and the cartoon cravers. If what you like is now (or has ever been) on TV, you'll find something of interest in this book.

The result of exhaustive research, back-breaking labor, and 92,458 cumulative hours of television viewing, this book is Volume I of *The World's Greatest TV Quiz.*

Though it is impossible to cram over twenty-five years of television programming into one book (or even a series of books, of which this is but the first—and, dare we add, a collector's item), we have attempted to cover as wide a field as possible in terms of variety. In other words, everything from game shows to science fiction is touched upon; and we feel a true TV Freak welcomes no less an effort.

Which brings us to the crux of the matter: the TV Freak.

Through an amazing display of naivete and basic lack of understanding of human nature, we are asking you to keep an accurate account of your performance on this test. If you receive a score of 80 per cent or better, then you qualify for the Certificate of TV Freakdom.

But more of that later. That's a whole book away for you, fellow trivianado, and we'll get to that in good time. For now, we ask that you assign yourself one point for every correct answer and keep your score as accurately as possible. (By the way, answers appear at the end of the book.)

Enough of this. Time to move on into the good stuff. So let your mind go, let your memories flow back. Have a good time and don't cheat too much.

Yours till Archie Bunker joins the ACLU,

The Authors

CHAPTER ONE

"And Your Mission, Should You Decide to Accept It . . ."

This book is about television.

It's sort of a contest between what you can remember and what we can remember. Some of the questions are fairly easy, others are fairly difficult, and some are downright impossible. Which questions fall into which category depends on how much you know (or think you know) about television.

As far as we can determine, this is the first quiz book dealing entirely with television trivia. Ideally, this book should make you ponder, make you laugh, and make you fondly remember a time when life was a lot less complex. It should also make you an expert on the subject—or, better still, enable you to make life miserable for anyone you can corner at the next cocktail party.

Any one of the above results would be extremely gratifying, but all we really hope is that you have as much fun reading this book as we had writing it.

The following short sections are examples of the kind of questions asked in the book and the manner in which they are asked. This first batch is simply *Completion,* or fill-in-the-blank, or whatever else you want to call it. We ask a question and you supply the answer (or answers). Occasionally we'll devote an entire chapter of questions to one famous TV series, like *I Love Lucy* or *Perry Mason.* But most often the completion questions will look like the following. See if you can answer them.

1) Who were the male and female stars of *The Thin Man*?
2) Who was the star of *Adventures in Paradise*?
3) Name the sports announcer on the original *Today Show.*
4) Name the original panel and host on *What's My Line?*
5) Name the male and female Indian characters on *Howdy Doody.*

You'll find the answers at the end of the book.

The next type of approach is called *Matching*, in which you match the name or title or character in the left column with the name or title or character in the right column. Okay? Usually the matching questions will deal with one specific category. In the ones presented here, the category is Westerns. Why not give them a try?

1) Paladin	a) Gene Barry
2) Bat Masterson	b) Will Hutchins
3) Stoney Burke	c) Richard Boone
4) Sugar Foot	d) Jack Lord

The next type is simply *True or False*. Read the statement and then decide if it is true or false. These can be tricky, so watch out. But remember, even if you only watch the symphony orchestra on Educational Television, you've got a fifty-fifty chance of guessing the correct answer. So try your luck and take a stab at the following:

1) Ollie was the alligator on *Kukla, Fran and Ollie.*
2) *Bourbon Street Beat* was a show about Dixieland music.
3) Richard Egan was the star of *Empire.*
4) Richard Egan was the star of *Redigo.*
5) Junior Samples are small boxes of Tide.

The last type of question is *Multiple Choice.* A question is asked and three or more alternative answers are given. Just pick the right answer (or answers) from those supplied. Some of these are tricky, so we caution you to be careful and answer each question thoughtfully. (Of course, once in a while we'll throw you a bone . . . out of the goodness of our hearts.)
Take a crack at the following examples:

1) Who was the star of *Zorro*?
   a) Duncan Renaldo b) Donald Diego
   c) Guy Williams d) Leo Carrillo

2) Who was host of *The $64,000 Question*?
   a) Jack Barry   b) Jack Narz
   c) Hal March   d) Sammy Ervin

3) What was the longest-running song on *Your Hit Parade*?
   a) "Shrimp Boats Are A-Comin' "
   b) "How Much Is That Doggie in the Window?"
   c) "The Three Little Fishes"
   d) "Hound Dog"

4) Name Wally's girlfriend on *Ozzie and Harriet.*
   a) Peaches   b) Ginger
   c) Mary Lou   d) Harriet

5) Which of the following did not appear on *Your Show of Shows*?
   a) Sid Caesar   b) Carl Reiner
   c) Mel Brooks   d) Imogene Coca
   e) Howard Morris

Now at the end of each section of the book, we'll pitch a group of *Mindbenders* at you. These are pretty tough questions, designed for the reader who is finding the regular group of questions too little a challenge to his massive intellect. If you can answer most of these Mindbenders, you're one helluva TV watcher.

Well, that's about it . . . except for the all-time *Super-Impossibles* at the end of this book. These are questions that. . . . Well, when you get to the end of the book, we'll let you know what these little babies are all about.

So now you're ready to go. Got your pencil ready? You are about to begin a journey into the abyss of television trivia . . . you are about to embark on a voyage into Volume I of *The World's Greatest TV Quiz.*

On your mark. . . . Get set. . . . GOOOOOOOO!

CHAPTER TWO

"I Love Lucy"

To get things off and running, let's begin with a group of questions about one of television's most well-known and well-loved series—*I Love Lucy*.

Lucille Ball and her show were responsible for cementing the family situation comedy format. And though some would argue that Lucy, the matriarch of television, deserves an entire book, let us hope that having the first position in this one will suffice.

"I Love Lucy"

1) Name the four principal stars and the characters they played.
2) What was Lucy's maiden name?
3) What was Ethel's maiden name?
4) Where was Lucy originally from?
5) Where was Ethel from?
6) What was Ricky's job and where did he work?
7) Fred and Ethel's current job in the series was . . .
8) What had they done before that?
9) What was Lucy's son's name?
10) Who was the old lady who lived upstairs and sometimes babysat?
11) What did Lucy's mother call her son-in-law?
12) What was Lucy's son's talent?
13) What was Ricky's theme song?
14) Where was Ricky from?
15) What was their address in Manhattan?

CHAPTER THREE

Private Eyes, Dicks, Shamuses, and Flatfeet

The backbone of the medium, private eyes have been a part of television since its inception. Even to this day, Americans can't get enough of this genre. Whodunits, cops-and-robbers, spies and counterspies, and mayhem in general will probably last as long as there is television.

Private Eyes, Dicks, Shamuses, and Flatfeet

Match the following with their respective shows:

1) Mother's	a) *Philip Marlowe*
2) Sam	b) *Dragnet*
3) Pax	c) *87th Precinct*
4) Erskine	d) *The Girl from U.N.C.L.E.*
5) Ben Alexander	e) *Hawaii Five-O*
6) Richard Long	f) *Richard Diamond*
7) Robert Conrad	g) *Peter Gunn*
8) Ben Gazzara	h) *Longstreet*
9) Paul Burke	i) *The FBI*
10) Mike Connors	j) *Hawaiian Eye*
11) Phillip Carey	k) *Arrest and Trial*
12) Noel Harrison	l) *77 Sunset Strip*
13) Gena Rowlands	m) *Tightrope*
14) Darren McGavin	n) *Mike Hammer*
15) James MacArthur	o) *Naked City*

CHAPTER FOUR

True and False: A Little Bit of Everything

True and False: A Little Bit of Everything

This section covers a wide variety of topics. Careless reader, beware!

True and False: A Little Bit of Everything

1) Mickey Finn wore garters on his shirtsleeves while he played the piano.
2) Bobby Rydell and Donna Loren were regulars on *The Milton Berle Show.*
3) Liberace's brother's name was Esteban.
4) Donna Reed's TV son and daughter each recorded a hit song.
5) Co-stars Michael Callan and Patricia Harty of *Occasional Wife* were married.
6) Rich Little was the neighbor on *Love on a Rooftop.*
7) Larry Storch played a sergeant on *F Troop.*
8) Paul Burke's first featured role in a TV series was in *Naked City.*
9) Jack Webb played the title role in the series *Pete Kelly's Blues.*
10) *Judd for the Defense* starred William Shatner.
11) Sam, on *Richard Diamond,* was played by Mary Tyler Moore.
12) Roy Thinnes could always identify Invaders by their pointed ears.
13) Richard Kimble was a dentist before he became The Fugitive.
14) Steve Reeves played Superman on television.
15) Lee J. Cobb played a lawyer on *The Young Lawyers.*

CHAPTER FIVE

They Clinked and Clanked and Barked and Clawed and Oinked and Galloped Their Way into Our Hearts

Television has long been a breeding ground for nonhuman characters. For years, we've been subjected to the antics of lovable dogs, cats, horses, pigs, machines, and even a few aliens. Most of these creatures were possessed of remarkable intellect—more so, sometimes, than the producers of the shows.

They Clinked and Clanked and Barked and Clawed and Oinked and Galloped Their Way into Our Hearts

1) Name the dog on *People's Choice.*
2) Name the pig on *Green Acres.*
3) Name four nonhuman characters on *Roy Rogers.*
4) Name the lion and the chimp on *Daktari.*
5) Name Hopalong Cassidy's horse.
6) Name Gene Autry's horse.
7) Name Blondie's dog.
8) Name the horse on *Mr. Ed.*
9) Who played Bob Cummings' "friend" on *My Living Doll?*
10) Name the dog on *My Three Sons.*
11) Name the dog on *Please Don't Eat the Daisies.*
12) Name Dennis the Menace's dog.
13) Name Tonto's horse.
14) Who was the voice of the car in *My Mother, the Car?*
15) Name Tom Terrific's dog.

CHAPTER SIX

They Went on to Bigger and Better Things

With the impact of television, a sizeable number of major stars have come into the public eye via the airwaves. This chapter deals with a small segment of these fortunates.

They Went on to Bigger and Better Things

1) Who portrayed Police Lieutenant Jacobi on *Peter Gunn*?
2) Who was the famous comedienne discovered by Garry Moore?
3) Who was the husband of Joan Davis on *I Married Joan*?
4) Who portrayed the three Men-on-the-Street on *The Steve Allen Show*?
5) Who starred as the bounty hunter on *Wanted: Dead or Alive*?
6) Who was Fess Parker's co-star on *Davy Crockett*?
7) Leslie Uggams first appeared on . . .
8) The boxing expert on *The $64,000 Question* was . . .
9) The piano-playing star of *Staccato* was . . .
10) Who played a corporal on the *Sgt. Bilko* show and went on to play Eric Von Zipper in American-International's beach party movies?
11) Who played Rowdy Yates?
12) Who played Jon Provost's mother on *Lassie* and later went on to win an Academy Award and an Emmy Award in the same year?
13) Who was the host of *G.E. Theatre*?
14) Who played the best-known student on *Our Miss Brooks*?
15) Who was Elaine May's partner?

CHAPTER SEVEN

"Right Here, on Our Stage . . ."

Television's answer to vaudeville, the musical variety show has also been a mainstay of American viewing. Stars were made, songs were introduced, and national fads were created. Everyone, it seems, still loves the same old song and dance.

"Right Here, on Our Stage . . ."

Read all the answers carefully and choose the correct one:

1) Who co-starred with the Lennon Sisters on their own show?
   a) Lawrence Welk
   b) B.B. King
   c) Eddie Cantor
   d) Jimmy Durante
   e) George Jessel

2) Who was the host of *Hootenanny*?
   a) Pete Seeger
   b) Bob Dylan
   c) Dylan Thomas
   d) Jack Linkletter
   e) Bill Sheehy

3) What was the first name of the Sullivan show?
   a) *Toast of the Town*
   b) *Ed*
   c) *Talk of the Town*
   d) *Hollywood Palace*
   e) *Stars on Parade*

4) Who was co-star of *The Garry Moore Show*?
   a) James Aubrey
   b) Durward Kirby
   c) Harvey Korman
   d) Johnny Olsen
   e) Sheldon Leonard

5) Who was the TW3 Girl (*That Was the Week That Was*)?
   a) Diahann Carroll
   b) Kate Smith
   c) Nancy Ames
   d) Marilyn Maye
   e) Donna Loren

6) On *The Andy Williams Show,* who always wanted cookies?
   a) Claudine Longet
   b) Gentle Ben
   c) Cookie Bear
   d) Donny Osmond
   e) Keebler Elves

7) Who was the songstress on *Sing Along with Mitch*?
   a) Dionne Warwicke
   b) Leslie Uggams
   c) Nancy Wilson
   d) Eartha Kitt
   e) Lena Horne
   f) Jim Bailey

8) Who was *not* a singer on *Your Hit Parade*?
   a) Giselle MacKenzie
   b) Steve Lawrence
   c) Snooky Lanson
   d) Dorothy Collins

9) Who was the host and star of *Washington Square*?
   a) Gene Kelly
   b) Fred Astaire
   c) Donald O'Connor
   d) Ray Bolger
   e) Arthur Murray
   f) Gower Champion

10) Who was Arthur Godfrey's most well-known singing protege?
    a) Julius LaRosa
    b) Jack Jones
    c) Gene Vincent
    d) Buddy Holly
    e) Vic Damone

11) How many seasons did the Emmy Award-winning, original *Bob Newhart Show* last?
    a) Five b) Three c) One d) Two e) Eighteen

12) What network originally carried *The Smothers Brothers* variety show?
    a) Dumont
    b) Blue Network
    c) NBC
    d) CBS
    e) Hughes

13) Who was the host of *Music Scene*?
    a) David Steinberg
    b) Bobby Sherman
    c) Jack Linkletter
    d) George Liberace
    e) Bobby Darin

14) Who was the host of *Shindig*?

a) Dick Clark
b) Bobby Sherman
c) Jack Jones
d) David Steinberg
e) Carroll O'Connor

15) "Letters, we get letters . . ." was a phrase heard on whose show?

a) Andy Williams
b) Dean Martin
c) Perry Como
d) Dinah Shore
e) Tom Jones

16) Name the dance group on *The Jackie Gleason Show.*

a) The June Taylor Dancers
b) The Peter Gennaro Dancers
c) The Rockettes
d) The Hullabaloo Dancers

17) Who was the drunk on *The Bill Cosby Show*?

a) Tom Brooks
b) Frank Fontaine
c) Foster Brooks
d) Stubby Kaye
e) Otis Campbell

18) What was Kate Smith's theme song?

a) "Come on a-My House"
b) "When the Moon Comes Over the Mountain"
c) "Yummy, Yummy, Yummy, I Got Love in My Tummy"
d) "God Bless America"
e) "Moon Over Miami"

19) Name the soap opera featured on *The Carol Burnett Show.*

a) "Those Who Care"
b) "Young Dr. Christian"
c) "As the Stomach Turns"
d) "As the Stomach Burns"
e) "As the Clock Turns"
f) "As the World Burns"

20) The Dean Martin-Jerry Lewis comedy hour was sponsored by:
   a) Bristol-Meyers
   b) Lever Brothers
   c) Colgate
   d) Carnation
   e) Procter and Gamble

CHAPTER EIGHT

Perry Mason:
He Always Got His Man . . . Off!

Every TV watcher headed for law school had already decided not to become a D.A., thanks to this popular lawyer show. Viewers were treated to confused plots, elabo-

All of which proves there must be something in consistency.

He Always Got His Man . . . Off!

1) Who played Perry Mason?
2) Who played Della Street?
3) What was the name of Perry Mason's receptionist?
4) What was the name of the police lieutenant?
5) Who portrayed him?
6) What was the name of the D.A.?
7) Who portrayed him?
8) What was the name of Mason's private investigator?
9) Who portrayed him?
10) In what city was Perry Mason located?
11) How many Emmies did the actor who portrayed Mason win?
12) Upon whose books was the series based?
13) How many cases did Mason lose?
14) How many cases did he win?
15) How many years did the show last?

CHAPTER NINE

Mindbenders #1

If they've been too easy so far—and even if they haven't—see what you can do with these questions.

Mindbenders #1

1) Name four people who portrayed Ellery Queen on a regular TV series.
2) Who replaced George Maharis on *Route 66* when he quit the show?
3) Who portrayed *Shane*?
4) In real life, Robert Culp's sister is . . .
5) Name the three stars of *Checkmate*.

CHAPTER TEN

Sidekicks: They Rode Together

Sidekicks were invaluable to your average TV hero. They provided comic relief, pulled the hero out of the boiling oil (always making him look good in the process), and usually had the unpleasant duty of standing by while the star got the girl (and the accolades). Their only rewards, in the end, were series residuals.

Sidekicks: They Rode Together

Part One

Match each hero with his sidekick:

1) Gene Autry	a) Burt Ward
2) Lone Ranger	b) Boo-boo
3) Guy Madison	c) Pat Brady
4) Adam West	d) Bob-a-lou
5) Napoleon Solo	e) Peter Brown
6) Roy Rogers	f) Chester Goode
7) Yogi Bear	g) Tonto
8) Fred Flintstone	h) Ethel Mertz
9) Yancy Derringer	i) Gillis
10) John Russell	j) Tony Randall
11) Matt Dillon	k) Pahoo-Ka-Ta-Wah
12) Quick Draw McGraw	l) Pat Buttram
13) Wally Cox	m) Ilya Kuryakin
14) Lucille Ricardo	n) Barney Rubble
15) Chester A. Riley	o) Andy Devine

Sidekicks: They Rode Together

Part Two

1) Jim West	a) Rocket J. Squirrel
2) Green Hornet	b) Buddy Ebsen
3) Dobie Gillis	c) Sid Melton
4) Andy Taylor	d) Bob Denver
5) Tod Stiles	e) Little John
6) Fess Parker	f) Kato
7) Captain Midnight	g) Norman Fell
8) Crusader Rabbit	h) Artemus Gordon
9) Danny Thomas	i) Buzz Murdock
10) Alan Hale, Jr.	j) Cullen Crabbe
11) Buster Crabbe	k) Maynard G. Krebs
12) Burt Reynolds	l) Ruff
13) Robin Hood	m) Barney Fife
14) Ready	n) Rags
15) Bullwinkle	o) Mudd

CHAPTER ELEVEN

The National Babysitter, or "Quit Bugging Me and Go Watch TV!"

Basically, this chapter is about children's shows. Early in the game, TV executives discovered that children were enthralled by the exaggerated movement of cartoon characters—and the exaggerated friendliness of children's show hosts. And, of course, parents loved children's television because it occupied the child's mind, doubling as playmate and pacifier.

Good, bad, or indifferent, the fact remains that half the population grew up with television. The following questions are about what they grew up with.

The National Babysitter, or, "Quit Bugging Me and Go Watch TV!"

1) Who played Dennis the Menace?
   - a) Jay North
   - b) Tony Dow
   - c) Mickey Dolenz
   - d) Joe Dearnes
   - e) Billy Campbell
   - f) Sabu

2) Who played Clarabelle on *Howdy Doody*?
   - a) Mr. Greenjeans
   - b) Alan Swift
   - c) Bob Keeshan
   - d) Emmett Kelly, Sr.
   - e) Emmett Kelly, Jr.

3) What was Beaver Cleaver's real name in the series *Leave It to Beaver*?
   - a) Eldridge
   - b) Theodore
   - c) Beef
   - d) William
   - e) Benita
   - f) Gopher

4) Who portrayed Commissioner Gordon on *Batman*?
   - a) Bob Kane
   - b) Alan Napier
   - c) Gale Gordon
   - d) Bob Sweeney
   - e) Neal Hamilton

5) Who first played Lois Lane on *Superman*?
   a) Lana Lang b) Lana Wood
   c) Noel Neill d) Cris Noel
   e) Phyllis Coates

6) Who created Beany and Cecil?
   a) Hanna-Barbera b) Mel Blanc
   c) Walt Disney d) Bob Clampett
   e) Jed Clampett

7) On *Huckleberry Hound,* Doggie Daddy's son was:
   a) Pooper Scooper b) Doggie Dooley
   c) Augie-Doggie d) Deputy Dawgie
   e) Arfie-Barfie

8) Who was the host of *Winky-Dink*?
   a) Pinky Lee b) Jack Barry
   c) Dan Enright d) Sam Levenson
   e) Don Herbert

9) The voice of Underdog was:
   a) Wally Cox b) Arnold Stang
   c) Sterling Holloway d) Lowell Thomas

10) Who portrayed Witchiepoo on *H.R. Puffinstuf*?
   a) Billie Burke b) Margaret Hamilton
   c) Billie Hayes d) Helen Hayes
   e) Lily Tomlin

11) Who played Sky King?
   a) Terry Lee b) Richard Egan
   c) Kirby Grant d) Grant Kirby
   e) George Kirby f) Cary Grant
   g) Lee Grant h) Ulysses S. Grant

12) Who was the star of *Jungle Jim*?
   a) Jon Hall b) Johnny Weissmuller
   c) Bobby Sheffield d) Mark Richman
   e) Sabu

13) Who played Rocky Jones, Space Ranger?

a) Buster Crabbe
b) Clayton Moore
c) Richard Crane
d) John Glenn
e) Guy Williams

14) Who was the female singer on Pinky Lee's show?

a) Donna Loren
b) Molly Bee
c) Denise Darcel
d) Florence Henderson

15) Who was the host of the *Mickey Mouse Club*?

a) Donald Duck
b) Tim Considine
c) Tommy Kirk
d) Jimmy Dodd
e) Cubby O'Brien
f) Ollie Gleickenhaus

CHAPTER TWELVE

The Mayberry Saga

The average TV viewer's roots are in rural America. Or at least he likes to think so. Realizing this, the networks bombarded the tube with shows featuring broad country humor and colorful, down-home characters. Since *The Andy Griffith Show* was one of the most popular of these series, we've included it.

The Mayberry Saga

1) What was Andy Griffith's occupation on the show?
2) In which city and state did the show take place?
3) Who portrayed Andy Griffith's son in the series and what was his name in the show?
4) What woman did they live with and who portrayed her?
5) Who played Andy's deputy and what was his name?
6) Who first ran the service station and who portrayed him?
7) This job was later taken by his cousin. What was his name and who played him?
8) Who played Ernest T. Bass?
9) What was the name of the town drunk—and who played him?
10) What was the name of the town barber—and who played him?
11) Andy ultimately married one of his girlfriends. What was her name on the show? Who played her?
12) What was her occupation?
13) Name Barney's girlfriend on the show—and who played her.
14) What did Barney carry in his left breast pocket?
15) Where did the townspeople go for entertainment?
16) Who played Howard Sprague?
17) Who played Emmett Clark? What was his occupation?

18) Who played the deputy that replaced Don Knotts?
19) How long was the show on the air?
20) How many maximum security cells were there in the sheriff's jail?

CHAPTER THIRTEEN

The Who, What, Where, How, Why, Name That, and Who Cares Matching Game

The same thing that made you buy this book made TV quiz shows work. The viewer became intellectually and emotionally involved with each show's questions and participants—and, of course, the cash and prizes were added incentives.

It is noteworthy, perhaps, that the quiz shows were responsible for the first scandals that would mar the fledgling television industry.

The Who, What, Where, How, Why, Name That, and Who Cares Matching Game

Match the game show with its host:

1) *You Bet Your Life*	a) Tom Kennedy
2) *Who Do You Trust?*	b) Jack Bailey
3) *People Are Funny*	c) Richard Hayes
4) *Queen for a Day*	d) Carl Reiner
5) *Treasure Hunt*	e) Bud Collyer
6) *Jeopardy*	f) Bud Collyer
7) The original *Price Is Right*	g) Mike Stokey
8) *Name That Tune*	h) Groucho Marx
9) *Beat the Clock*	i) Garry Moore
10) *To Tell the Truth*	j) Art Linkletter
11) *The Celebrity Game*	k) Jan Murray
12) *College Bowl*	l) Johnny Carson
13) *Stump the Stars*	m) Bill Cullen
14) *You Don't Say*	n) Art Fleming
15) *I've Got a Secret*	o) Allen Ludden

CHAPTER FOURTEEN

What They Did Besides Live Next Door

With the evolution of the second banana, the next-door neighbor developed into such an integral part of the average situation comedy that our memories of them—and of what they did for a living—stay fresh. Try these questions and see.

What They Did Besides Live Next Door

1) Occupation of the next-door neighbor on *The Dick Van Dyke Show*:
   a) Dentist
   b) Chiropractor
   c) High school coach
   d) Sewer worker

2) Thorney's occupation on *Ozzie and Harriet*:
   a) Police sergeant
   b) Grocer
   c) Same as Ozzie's
   d) Gardener

3) What was Eddie Haskell's occupation on *Leave It to Beaver*?
   a) Cheese eater
   b) Professional punk
   c) Student
   d) Undercover narc

4) Fred Mertz's occupation on *I Love Lucy*:
   a) Plumber
   b) Interpreter
   c) Landlord
   d) Former Nazi spy

5) Frank Lorenzo's occupation on *All in the Family*:
   a) Domestic engineer
   b) Construction laborer
   c) Hit Man
   d) Pizza cutter

6) On Andy Griffith's show, Gomer Pyle was one of the following:
   a) Brain surgeon
   b) Gas station attendant
   c) Electrician
   d) House painter

7) Art Carney's occupation on *The Honeymooners*:
   a) Bus driver
   b) Domestic engineer
   c) Sewer worker
   d) Met conductor

8) Rhoda's occupation on *The Mary Tyler Moore Show*:
   a) Department store window dresser
   b) Dress designer
   c) Exotic dancer
   d) Cartoonist

9) On *Wendy and Me*, the occupation of Connie Stevens' husband:
   a) Cartoonist
   b) Dress designer
   c) Airline pilot
   d) Doctor
   e) Up-and-coming young attorney

10) What did Gillis do in *The Life of Riley*?
   a) Factory worker
   b) Dentist
   c) Sculptor
   d) Electrician

CHAPTER FIFTEEN

"The Dick Van Dyke Show"

Frankly, this is our all-time favorite TV situation comedy. All facets of the show were above average: the direction, writing, characterization, and talent. Moreover, like the best sitcoms, it had an excellent supporting cast and tight plot development. Combine these elements with well-drawn interrelationships among the characters and truly classic comedic situations, and you have *The Dick Van Dyke Show.*

"The Dick Van Dyke Show"

1) What character did Dick Van Dyke portray?
2) What did he do for a living?
3) What was his wife's name in the series?
4) Who portrayed his wife?
5) What was her occupation before their marriage?
6) Where did they meet?
7) What were the character names of their next-door neighbors?
8) Who portrayed them?
9) What was the name of Dick Van Dyke's son on the show?
10) What was the name of the neighbors' son?
11) What character did Morey Amsterdam portray?
12) What character did Rose Marie portray?
13) What was the name of Morey Amsterdam's wife in the series?
14) Name Rose Marie's boyfriend in the series.
15) What was the name of the TV show they worked on?
16) Who portrayed the star of that show?
17) Morey Amsterdam constantly harassed the producer. Who was he?
18) Who portrayed him?
19) What was his relationship to the star of the show?
20) Where did Dick Van Dyke live?

CHAPTER SIXTEEN

Hosts, Voices, and Narrators

People never think of them as stars, but sometimes the hosts, offscreen voices, and narrators really made the show. For years, whether seen or unseen, the well-trained TV voice has sold, cajoled, advised, badgered, created a mood, or simply told a story. Though primarily a visual medium, without the sound to enhance sight and motion, television would be nothing more than images moving on a screen.

Hosts, Voices, and Narrators

1) Who was the narrator on both *The Fugitive* and *Bullwinkle*?
2) Who was the narrator for *Fractured Fairy Tales*?
3) Who was the voice of Kukla, Ollie, and Beulah the Witch?
4) Who narrated *The Untouchables*?
5) Who was the narrator on *Dragnet*?
6) Who was the announcer of *To Tell the Truth*?
7) Who was the host of *Omnibus*?
8) Who was the announcer on *Let's Make a Deal*?
9) Who was the narrator on *People's Choice*?
10) Who was Jack Paar's announcer on *The Tonight Show*?
11) Who was the host and sometime star of *Medic*?
12) Who was the announcer on the *Kraft Music Hall*?
13) Who was Joey Bishop's announcer on his nighttime show?
14) Who was the host of *Science Fiction Theatre*?
15) What current sports commentator formerly narrated *The Verdict Is Yours*?
16) Who was the narrator on *The Millionaire*?
17) Who was the voice of Mr. Magoo?
18) Who was the voice of Charlie the Tuna?
19) Name the announcer on Arthur Godfrey's program.
20) Who was the announcer/narrator/philosopher on *Ben Casey*?

CHAPTER SEVENTEEN

Mindbenders #2

Here's another batch of Mindbenders, just so you don't get bored.

Mindbenders #2

1) Who sponsored *Big Top*?
2) Who played the title role of *Texas John Slaughter*?
3) Who played Spring Byington's best friend on *December Bride*?
4) Who played the title role in *I Remember Mama*?
5) Who was the announcer on *You Bet Your Life*?

CHAPTER EIGHTEEN

The "Who's Who" of Westerns

The first television Westerns were based upon little more than rehashed storylines from old Republic B-movies—symbolized by the singing cowboy, the jovial sidekick, or "Heigh-O, Silver! Awayyyy!" As the TV Western evolved and the screen became saturated with ricocheting bullets, stampeding herds, and a myriad of stuntmen biting the dust, the genre as a whole improved. The plots deviated from the usual good guy vs. bad guy and pursued more adult themes; gimmick-ladened heroes gave way to leading men with more carefully-etched characterizations; tighter close-ups and what the networks call "more meaningful relationships" soon replaced the endless scenes of marauding Indians, frontier cattle rustlers, and infamous outlaw gangs. But when you think of TV Westerns, what still comes to mind are showdowns on Main Street, faithful Indian companions, and cereal shot from guns.

The "Who's Who" of Westerns

1) Who played Tonto?
2) Who played Paladin?
3) Who starred in *The Texan*?
4) Who starred in *The Lawman*?
5) Who played Jim Bowie?
6) Who played Sugarfoot?
7) Who was the star of *Riverboat*?
8) Who starred in *Restless Gun*?
9) Who were the stars of *Rawhide*?
10) Who played Temple Houston?
11) Who were the stars of *Dakotas*?
12) Who starred in *Bronco*?
13) Who was the star of *Cheyenne*?
14) Who were the stars of *Dundee and the Culhane*?
15) Name four adult stars of *Laramie*.
16) Who played Annie Oakley?
17) Who played Stoney Burke?

18) Who played the Cisco Kid?
19) Who starred in *The Adventures of Judge Roy Bean*?
20) Who played Bat Masterson?
21) Who starred in *Black Saddle*?
22) Who starred in *Buckskin*?
23) Who played in *Frontier Doctor*?
24) Who starred in *Guns of Will Sonnett*?
25) Who was the star of *Cade's County*?
26) Who starred in *Law of the Plainsman*?
27) Who were the two stars of *The Legend of Jesse James*?
28) Who starred in *Man Without a Gun*?
29) Who played the part of Lucas McCain's son on *The Rifleman*?
30) Who were the stars of *Tombstone Territory*?
31) Who played the wagon masters of *Wagon Train*?
32) Who was the star of *Trackdown*?
33) Who were the stars of *The Outcasts*?
34) Name four American stars of *Laredo.*
35) Who was the star of *Iron Horse*?

CHAPTER NINETEEN

Nemeses, Foils, and Bad Guys

Let's face it—what would a good guy be without a bad guy? The very crux of all drama is conflict; and television scripts, basically melodramatic in the classic sense, faithfully adhere to this principle. Although the television good guy got all the money and the stardom, his foil usually had a more satisfying and fun role. From the waddling antics of "The Penguin," to the more sinister schemes of Dr. Miguelito Loveless, to the absolutely fiendish masterplans of THRUSH Central, the television antagonist traditionally commanded the greatest reaction from the TV viewer.

Nemeses, foils, and bad guys—we tip our black hats to your memory.

Nemeses, Foils, and Bad Guys

Part One

Match the bad guy with the appropriate good guy:

1) Doctor Smith	a) Phil Silvers
2) Dr. Miguelito Loveless	b) Darren Stevens
3) Snidely Whiplash	c) Steve McGarrett
4) Crabby Appleton	d) Wiley Coyote
5) Phineas T. Bluster	e) Herbert Philbrick
6) THRUSH	f) The Robinson family
7) Wo Fat	g) Bullwinkle
8) The Penguin	h) James West
9) Boris and Natasha	i) Col. Hogan
10) Communist Party	j) Howdy Doody
11) Colonel Klink	k) Tom Terrific
12) Paul Ford	l) Dudley Do-Right
13) Al Capone	m) U.N.C.L.E.
14) Endora	n) Batman
15) Roadrunner	o) Elliot Ness

Nemeses, Foils, and Bad Guys

Part Two

1) Klingons	a) King Leonardo
2) Gerrard	b) Perry Mason
3) Binghamton	c) Danny Williams
4) Dennis the Menace	d) Federation officers
5) Avery Schreiber	e) Gomer Pyle
6) KAOS	f) Oliver Douglas
7) Screaming Chicken	g) The Fugitive
8) Hamilton Burger	h) Zorro
9) Sergeant Carter	i) The Clampetts
10) Mr. Hainey	j) McHale
11) Mr. Drysdale	k) Jerry Van Dyke
12) Aaron Stemple	l) CONTROL
13) Uncle Tonoose	m) Mr. Wilson
14) The Commandante	n) F Troop
15) Biggie Rat	o) Jason Bolt

CHAPTER TWENTY

"Whaddaya Mean, War Is Hell?" or, "Who Needs a Three-Day Pass? I'll Take Residuals!"

The military experience was developed into a comedy form that everyone could enjoy. If you'd been in the service, you knew a McHale, a Hogan, or a Sergeant Carter—and if you hadn't, you felt sure you would have. Army life was a microcosm of all structured society, so what the Bilkos, the Hawkeye Pierces, and the Ensign Pulvers were ultimately demonstrating was their ability to survive in spite of the service.

And they sure made it seem like fun.

"Whaddaya Mean, War Is Hell?"

1) Who played Colonel Hall on *The Phil Silvers Show*?
   a) Phil Ford
   b) Werner Klemperer
   c) Paul Ford
   d) Paul Douglas
   e) Roscoe Karns

2) Who played Marion Butnick in the World War II Navy sitcom called *Broadsides*?
   a) Kathy Nolan
   b) Lois Roberts
   c) Joan Staley
   d) Sheila James
   e) Jim Bailey
   f) Jimmy Boyd

3) Who was the star of the TV series *No Time for Sergeants*?
   a) Andy Griffith
   b) Jim Nabors
   c) Lew Ayres
   d) Sammy Jackson
   e) Frank Carter

4) What was the PT boat number on *McHale's Navy*?
   a) 109 b) 72 c) 51 d) 73 e) 714 f) 37

5) Who played Juliet Prowse's sergeant husband in *Mona McClusky*?
   a) Roger Smith
   b) Dennis Cole
   c) Dick Sargent
   d) Larry Hagman
   e) Denny Miller

6) Who played Ensign O'Toole?
   a) Beau Bridges
   b) Robert Walker, Jr.
   c) Jack Lemmon
   d) Dean Jones
   e) Tim Conway

7) Name the stars of *The Soldiers*:
   a) George Lindsey and Jim Nabors
   b) Tom D'Andrea and Hal March
   c) Maurice Gosfield and Harvey Lembeck
   d) Larry Storch and Forrest Tucker
   e) Jean Seberg and Ingrid Bergman

8) In *M*A*S*H,* what was Colonel Blake's alma mater?
   a) West Point
   b) V.M.I.
   c) Ding Dong School
   d) Illinois
   e) Michigan State
   f) University of Pittsburgh

9) Who played Mr. Roberts?
   a) Roger Perry
   b) Roger Smith
   c) Roger Bowman
   d) Fred Rogers
   e) Roy Rogers

10) Who played Major Healy on *I Dream of Jeanie*?
   a) James Daly
   b) Bill Daily
   c) Jack Haley
   d) William Paley
   e) Arthur Hailey

11) What was Hennesey's profession in the Navy?
   a) Brain surgeon
   b) Bandleader
   c) Attorney
   d) Hygenist
   e) Dentist
   f) Undertaker

12) Hennesey's girlfriend was played by:
   a) Roscoe Karns
   b) Kathy Nolan
   c) Melody Patterson
   d) Lola Albright
   e) Abby Dalton
   f) Sue Anne Langdon

13) What was Colonel Hogan's first name?

a) Ben
b) Steve
c) Robert
d) Werner
e) Colonel

14) Who played the ranking army officer on board *The Wackiest Ship in the Army*?

a) Gary Collins
b) Jack Warden
c) Rick Nelson
d) Joe Flynn
e) Monte Markham

15) What was the name of the prisoner-of-war camp in *Hogan's Heroes*?

a) Camp Grenada
b) Camp David
c) Camp Runamuck
d) Stalag 13
e) Stalag 17

16) What was the name of the fort on *F Troop*?

a) Fort Courage
b) Fort Courageous
c) Fort Etude
d) Fort Apache
e) Fort Knox

17) What was McHale's first name?

a) Mac
b) Heywood
c) Bill
d) Quentin
e) Marty

18) What cartoon character exclamation did Gomer Pyle always quote when he was excited?

a) "Great Caesar's Ghost!"
b) "Holey Moley!"
c) "Shazam!"
d) "Leapin' Lizards!"
e) "Jeepers Creepers!"

19) What type of military equipment was Corporal O'Reilly in *M*A*S*H* nicknamed after?

a) Jeep
b) Machine Gun
c) Turret
d) Radar
e) Walkie-Talkie
f) Mae West

20) Where was Gomer Pyle stationed?
    a) Camp Budingen
    b) Camp Henderson
    c) Fort Huachuca
    d) Camp Swampy
    e) Camp Smokey

CHAPTER TWENTY-ONE

"Topper"

Topper was fun. To say anything more would not be in keeping with the spirit of this chapter.

"Topper"

1) Who played Topper?
2) Who played his wife?
3) What was unusual about Topper's two close friends?
4) Why did they live in the house?
5) What were their names on the show?
6) Who played them?
7) What kind of dog did they own?
8) What was the dog's name?
9) Other than his being a ghost, what was the dog's idiosyncrasy?
10) How did the ghosts become ghosts?

CHAPTER TWENTY-TWO

You Remember Them for This . . .

This next series of true-or-false questions deal with actors and the roles with which they were associated. For all of you that are doing well so far, watch out—we threw some real zingers in here.

You Remember Them for This . . .

True or false:

1) Doug McClure appeared in *Overland Trail.*
2) Jack Webb's badge was number 741.
3) Hayley Mills starred in *Nanny and the Professor.*
4) Walter Brennan starred in *Tycoon.*
5) Lloyd Bridges starred in *The Loner.*
6) Doug McClure starred in *The Virginian.*
7) Chuck Connors owned a cattle ranch in *Branded.*
8) Tim Conway and Joe Flynn starred in two shows together.
9) Robert Reed starred in *The Defenders* and *The Brady Bunch.*
10) Gene Barry played Doc Holliday.
11) Doug McClure starred in *Search.*
12) Ann Prentiss starred with Dick Benjamin in *He and She.*
13) Ray Milland played a detective named Markham.
14) Doug McClure starred in *Checkmate.*
15) Walter Brennan starred in *To Rome with Love.*
16) Robert Young starred in *Father Knows Best, Window on Main Street,* and *Marcus Welby, M.D.*
17) Cara Williams starred as Gladys in *December Bride.*
18) In real life, Kit Carson was married to Della Street.
19) *A Man Called Shenandoah* starred Robert Fuller.
20) Burt Reynolds starred or co-starred in *Dan August, Hawk, Gunsmoke,* and *Riverboat.*
21) Sammy Spear was Bob Hope's bandleader.
22) In both her series, Don Porter played Ann Sothern's boss.

23) Ann B. Davis won an Emmy Award for playing Schultzy on Bob Cummings' second TV series.
24) *Peyton Place* was the only prime-time TV show on more than once a week.
25) Herbert Philbrick played the lead in the series *I Led Three Lives.*

CHAPTER TWENTY-THREE

"The Butler Did It"

An incredible number of series used as a central character (or for strong support) colorful domestics, who usually shared a deeper insight into human nature than their employers. Syndicated in foreign lands, these shows probably gave the rest of the world the impression that we had not only a chicken in every pot and two cars in every garage, but also a butler in every parlor.

"The Butler Did It"

1) Who was the butler on *Batman,* and who played him?
2) Who played Don De Fore's maid?
3) Who was the butler on *Family Affair,* and who played him?
4) Who was houseboy and chauffeur to Brett Reid, and who played him?
5) Who was the cook on *Bonanza*?
6) Who was the housekeeper on *The Courtship of Eddie's Father*?
7) Who played the nanny on *Nanny and the Professor*?
8) Who was the butler on the Kleenex Napkin commercials?
9) Who was the butler on *The Big Valley*?
10) Who played housekeeper on *The Brady Bunch*?
11) Who portrayed the housekeeper on *McMillan and Wife,* and what is her character's name?
12) Name the maid portrayed by Imogene Coca.
13) Name the butler on *Valentine's Day,* and who played him.
14) Who portrayed the domestics on *The Good Life*?
15) Who was the famous domestic who also appeared on Merv Griffin?

CHAPTER TWENTY-FOUR

"Answers, We've Got Answers . . ."

Some of our favorite people are included in this group of multiple choice questions. Make sure you read all of the answers given or else you'll miss a lot of the fun.

"Answers, We've Got Answers . . ."

Multiple choice:

1) Who were Pete and Gladys?
   - a) Henry Morgan and Cara Williams
   - b) Harry Morgan and Cara Williams
   - c) Dennis Morgan and Gwen Verdon
   - d) Harry Morgan and Imogene Coca
   - e) Harry Morgan and Verna Felton

2) Who played Burns and Allen's son on their TV series?
   - a) Bill Campbell
   - b) Jack Burns
   - c) Ronny Schell
   - d) Ronny Burns
   - e) George Burns, Jr.

3) What was David Nelson's bride's maiden name?
   - a) Kris Harmon
   - b) June Harmon
   - c) June Blair
   - d) Brenda Sykes

4) Who was Lassie's original owner?
   - a) Jon Provost
   - b) Tommy Rettig
   - c) Elizabeth Taylor
   - d) Jay North
   - e) Mickey Dolenz

5) Name two that were not owners of the Shiloh Ranch.
   - a) Ed Begley
   - b) Lorne Greene
   - c) Lee J. Cobb
   - d) John McIntire
   - e) Charles Bickford

6) Who starred in *The Detectives*?
   a) Robert Lansing
   b) Gerald O'Laughlin
   c) Robert Taylor
   d) Joe E. Ross
   e) Simon Oakland

7) Who was host/narrator of *The Big Story*?
   a) Richard Boone
   b) Dane Clark
   c) Walter Winchell
   d) Burgess Meredith

8) Who was the host of *Alcoa Theatre*?
   a) Robert Montgomery
   b) David Niven
   c) Loretta Young
   d) Fred Astaire
   e) Sebastian Cabot

9) *The Law and Mr. Jones* starred:
   a) James Whitmore
   b) William Shatner
   c) Richard Crenna
   d) Carl Betz
   e) Ralph Bellamy

10) What was Alan Young's name on *Mr. Ed*?
   a) Eddie Arcaro
   b) Wilbur Post
   c) Chester Gould
   d) Henry Fife
   e) Eddie Brownstein

11) Who played Danny Thomas' wife on *Make Room for Grand-Daddy*?
   a) Marjorie Lord
   b) Lee Meriwether
   c) Patricia Crowley
   d) Elsa Maxwell

12) Who was the star of *Rescue Eight*?
   a) Rod Cameron
   b) Jim Davis
   c) Glenn Corbett
   d) Kenneth Tobey

13) Who was Jim Backus's female co-star in *Hot off the Wire*?
   a) Eve Arden
   b) Joan Davis
   c) Ann B. Davis
   d) Nita Talbot

14) Who starred in *The Double Life of Henry Phyfe*?
   a) George Gobel
   b) Red Skelton
   c) Red Buttons
   d) Wally Cox

15) Who did Jimmy Durante say goodnight to at the end of his show?
   a) Bess Truman
   b) Mrs. Kelly
   c) Mrs. Durante
   d) Mrs. Calabash

16) Who starred in *Blue Light*?
   a) Robert Goulet
   b) Robert Lansing
   c) David Hedison
   d) Anne Francis

17) Michael Anderson, Jr., and Barbara Hershey starred in what series?
   a) *The Californians*
   b) *The Monroes*
   c) *Overland Trail*
   d) *Empire*

18) Who was the host of *Zane Grey Theatre*?
   a) Dale Robertson
   b) Ronald Reagan
   c) Dick Powell
   d) The Old Ranger
   e) Yosemite Sam
   f) Zane Grey

19) Who starred as Tarzan?
   a) Jock Mahoney
   b) Gordon Scott
   c) J. Fred Muggs
   d) Ron Ely
   e) Buster Crabbe
   f) Mike Henry

20) Why did the Beverly Hillbillies move to Beverly Hills?
   a) They wanted to get into the movies.
   b) Jed Clampett had health problems.
   c) That's where their car broke down.
   d) Jed had discovered oil.
   e) They won a two-week, all-expenses-paid trip to Hollywood and lost their return-trip ticket.

CHAPTER TWENTY-FIVE

Mindbenders #3

If you think this test has been hard so far, you'd better skip these and go on to Chapter Twenty-Six.

Mindbenders #3

1) Name the host and original panel of *I've Got a Secret.*
2) Who was the star of *Range Rider*?
3) Name the character Steve McQueen played in *Wanted: Dead or Alive.*
4) Who played the little boy on *Hazel*?
5) Who was the star of *Hotel de Paree*?

CHAPTER TWENTY-SEVEN

"Why Not?"

This has been television's most invincible western. All the stalwarts are present: the strong, silent marshal, the saloon owner, the deputy, the town doctor, the bartender, and—of course—the town character. Their frontier milieu was an 1870s Naked City, where there were at least eight million stories . . . or so it seemed.

"Gunsmoke"

1) Who was the show's principal star?
2) Who played Miss Kitty?
3) What was Miss Kitty's last name?
4) Name her saloon.
5) What city and state did the series take place in?
6) Who played the part of Doc?
7) What was his last name?
8) Who played Chester?
9) What was his last name?
10) Chester was replaced by what character?
11) Who played him?
12) What was his last name?
13) Who played the half-breed blacksmith?
14) Who played Sam the bartender?
15) What year did the show start on TV?

CHAPTER TWENTY-SEVEN

"Why Not?"

Why not, indeed? This is the last series of true-or-false questions in the book, so give it your best shot.

"Why Not?"

True or false:

1) Joe Flynn was a co-star of *McHale's Navy.*
2) Lassie portrays a female collie.
3) Sheb Wooley co-starred in *Rawhide* and sang "Purple People Eater."
4) Stuart Whitman starred in *Cimarron City.*
5) One wired Paladin in San Diego.
6) Henry Fonda played the title role on *The Deputy.*
7) The part of Catwoman on the *Batman* series was played by Lee Meriwether.
8) Mr. Lucky owned a floating gambling casino off the coast of Monte Carlo.
9) Ken Curtis was a co-star of *Whirlybirds.*
10) The title role in *Dobie Gillis* was portrayed by Darryl Hickman.
11) Zasu Pitts was co-star of *My Little Margie.*
12) Yukon King's master's name was Preston.
13) In *87th Precinct,* Robert Lansing's wife was a deaf mute.
14) Flubadub was a duck-billed platypus.
15) Warner Anderson was the star of *The Line-Up.*

CHAPTER TWENTY-EIGHT

". . . We've Got Lots and Lots of Answers!"

This is another series of multiple choice questions. We give you a choice, not an echo.

". . . We've Got Lots and Lots of Answers!"

1) Who was the star of *International Airport*?
   - a) Lloyd Nolan
   - b) Lloyd Bridges
   - c) Eddie Rickenbacker
   - d) Burt Lancaster

2) Which one was not a series featuring Richard Crenna?
   - a) *The Real McCoys*
   - b) *Our Miss Brooks*
   - c) *Judd for the Defense*
   - d) *Slattery's People*

3) E. G. Marshall was a lawyer on:
   - a) *The Bold Ones*
   - b) *Divorce Court*
   - c) *Arrest and Trial*
   - d) *The Defenders*

4) On *Harrigan and Son,* Pat O'Brien's partner was:
   - a) Pat Harrington
   - b) Bill Bixby
   - c) Charlie Coats
   - d) Roger Perry

5) Who played the surly son on *The Big Valley*?
   - a) Jeff Davidson
   - b) Dack Rambo
   - c) Lee Majors
   - d) Peter Breck
   - e) Richard Long

6) Which was *not* a Mark VII Production?
   - a) *Emergency*
   - b) *The D.A.*
   - c) *87th Precinct*
   - d) *Adam-12*

7) Who was the star of *The Baileys of Balboa*?
   - a) Joan Blondell
   - b) Kathy Nolan
   - c) Judy Carne
   - d) Tina Louise
   - e) Dorothy Lamour

8) Who played the female lead on *Bachelor Father*?
   a) Patty McCormack
   b) Patty Duke
   c) Lily St. Cyr
   d) Noreen Corcoran
   e) Angela Cartwright

9) Roy Rogers' singing group was:
   a) The Pennsylvanians
   b) The Sons of the Pioneers
   c) The Cumberlands
   d) The Red River Ramblers
   e) Peter, Paul, and Mary

10) Who played Mr. Drysdale on *The Beverly Hillbillies*?
   a) Raymond Bailey
   b) Gale Gordon
   c) Nancy Culp
   d) Andrew Duggan

CHAPTER TWENTY-NINE

"Star Trek"

Star Trek can boast one of television's most loyal (and vocal) cult followings. When threatened with cancelation at the end of its first season, the show was reportedly saved from the network ax by a barrage of protest letters, phone calls, and student demonstrations in front of the NBC building. Though the mighty starship's five-year mission was aborted at the end of three, the show has continued to sustain its many fans through wide syndication.

Star Trek had much for which it should be commended: it was a real attempt at adult science fiction, using well-drawn characterizations and believable interaction between the principals instead of depending solely upon monsters, ray guns, and special effects gimmicks. Aliens had motivations other than universal conquest, tempers flared on the bridge, and people generally behaved like people; the only difference was that it took place two hundred years in the future. In Mr. Spock, *Star Trek* also featured one of television's most bizarre fictional characters.

Though sometimes flawed with melodramatic excess and painfully obvious anachronisms, *Star Trek* possessed a certain mystique that has made it a memorable series.

"Star Trek"

1) Who created *Star Trek*?
2) Who starred as Captain Kirk?
3) Who played Mr. Spock?
4) Where was he from?
5) Who portrayed Dr. McCoy?
6) What was his nickname?
7) What was the name of his head nurse?
8) Who portrayed her?
9) What was the name of the navigator/helmsman?
10) Who portrayed him?

11) What was the name of the chief engineer?
12) Who portrayed him?
13) Who was the communications officer?
14) Who played this role?
15) To whom did the captain answer?
16) What was the Prime Directive?
17) What was the organization of planets called?
18) Who were usually the bad guys in the series?
19) What was Spock's specialty in hand-to-hand combat?
20) What were the hand weapons used by the crew?
21) How did the crew get from the ship to a planet?
22) Who were Spock's parents?
23) Who played Spock's mother?
24) A small vehicle was docked within the hull of the starship and used for short trips. What was it called?
25) What was the name of the starship itself?

CHAPTER THIRTY

"The Play's the Thing"—and It Was Live

The question most frequently asked by critics and viewers alike is "What happened to good television drama?" Coincidentally, the discontinuation of weekly quality drama came at the same time that the networks moved their productions from New York to Hollywood. Television's product therefore lost the benefits of the Broadway experience and came under the creative control of the Hollywood image-makers. In the 1950s, new writers and directors looked to television as a bright new medium in which to develop their craft. Thus, TV forced the movies into becoming a better, more articulate art form, and it was only natural that the lure of bigger money would draw these new talents away from television.

There were, of course, other reasons why "good" drama vanished from the airwaves. Astronomical production costs, networks' showing of feature films, and, in some cases, low ratings all contributed to this demise. To be commercially successful, the TV industry has to appeal to a mass audience. Since a segment of *Hee Haw* will outdraw a *Hallmark Hall of Fame* production by 50-to-1 in the ratings, the contention that TV viewers want better TV than they are getting would appear to be refuted. In the end then, what really killed good television was the viewers.

"The Play's the Thing"—and It Was Live

1) Who played Cyrano de Bergerac on *The Philco-Goodyear Television Playhouse*?
2) Who starred in *Marty* on television?
3) Who played the boxer in *Requiem for a Heavyweight*?
4) Who starred in *A Long Time till Dawn* on *The Kraft Television Theatre*?
5) Who was the creator of *Profiles in Courage*?

6) Who was the director of *A Night to Remember*?
7) Who was kicked off to fame in *The Singing Idol,* in which he sang his only hit song?
8) Who played the starring role in the *U.S. Steel Hour* presentation of *No Time for Sergeants*?
9) Who hosted *Matinee Theatre*?
10) Who played Duke Mantee in the TV version of *The Petrified Forest*?
11) Who played Mr. Lincoln in a continuing series on *Omnibus*?
12) What do these people have in common: Ethel Barrymore, Maxie Rosenbloom, Charlie Ruggles, Inger Stevens, Conrad Hilton, Monty Wooley, and Evelyn Rudie?
13) What do these shows have in common: *Marty, Requiem for a Heavyweight, The Miracle Worker, Judgment at Nuremburg,* and *Days of Wine and Roses*?
14) Who played the title role in *What Makes Sammy Run?*
15) What do these titles have in common: *A Tale of Two Cities, For Whom the Bell Tolls, Body and Soul,* and *Harvey*?

CHAPTER THIRTY-ONE

"Goodnight, David . . . Goodnight, Chet . . . Goodnight, Walter . . . Goodnight, Doug . . . Goodnight, Ted . . . Goodnight, Lawrence . . . Goodnight, Ed . . . Goodnight, Tom . . . Goodnight, Dick . . . Goodnight, Harry . . . Goodnight, Irene . . . Goodnight . . ."

Though the network news departments will contend that their reporters are professional journalists, it's no secret that they are in show business as well, and that, like all other TV personalities, they are subject to ratings. The point might also be made that—if a national credibility poll were conducted—Walter Cronkite, John Chancellor, and Harry Reasoner would undoubtedly prove to be the three most believed men in America. The ramifications of this fact are obvious.

To demonstrate the degree to which newsmen have developed as personalities, we submit that each has become noted for a unique "intro" or close to his newscast. Just as "Thanks for the Memory" is identified with Bob Hope, and a pie in the face with Soupy Sales, so does each newsman have his catch-phrase, his own distinct opening or closing line; in other words, his shtick.

"Goodnight, David . . . Goodnight, Chet . . ."

Name the TV newsman associated with the phrase used to open or close his newscast:

1) "Goodnight . . . and good luck."
2) "And that's the way it is, Friday . . ."
3) "This is ______, on the road."
4) "Good evening, Mr. and Mrs. North America and all the ships at sea . . ."
5) "This is ______ with the news."
6) "And a good evening to you . . ."
7) "This is ______, for television's longest running interview show . . ." (We want the name of the moderator, not the show.)
8) "Peace."
9) "Glad we could get together."
10) "Goodnight and good newt." (That's right—"Goodnight and good newt!")

CHAPTER THIRTY-TWO

"Filling In for Johnny Tonight . . ."

In the old days, insomniacs and third-shift workers had a problem. The only programs available were sermonettes, and the number one song on the late-night hit parade was either "The Star-Spangled Banner" or "America the Beautiful."

To break up the monotony of old Monogram B-movies, the late-night talk show was instituted. It has been with us ever since. The talk show operated on a low budget and specialized in discovering new talent, merchandising the latest best-seller, and thrusting the cleavage of budding starlets into the bedrooms of America. In its worst moments, the late-night talk show can prompt even the most atheistic viewer into switching to a sermonette; at its best, it is human, spontaneous, and a legitimate testing ground for a performer's new material.

"Filling In for Johnny Tonight . . ."

1) Who used a shotgun microphone to pick up questions from members of his audience?
2) Who was Johnny Carson's original bandleader?
3) Who hosted the original *Tonight Show*?
4) Who was the second host of the *Tonight Show*?
5) Who was the female French guest star often seen on the *Tonight Show*?
6) Whose trademark was a clipboard?
7) Name the talk show host whose theme was "Oh, What a Lovely Bunch of Coconuts"?
8) Who started out as a writer for Jack Paar and went on to host his own late-night show?
9) Name the daytime talk show which features a weekly co-host.
10) The star of this daytime talk show was married to the star of *Cimarron City*. (We'll give you a hint—it's not Sonny Tufts.)
11) Name the fifteen-year-old singer on the daytime *Tennessee Ernie Ford Show*.

12) Who was the star of the *Home* show?
13) Who was Garry Moore's announcer/sidekick?
14) Who hosted a weekly, two-hour talk show on Saturday night?
15) Who is the most loyal talk show fan in America?

CHAPTER THIRTY-THREE

Mindbenders #4

As a practice run before attempting the Super-Impossibles, we ask you to take a crack at five more of the now-infamous Mindbenders.

Mindbenders #4

1) Name the three children and who portrayed them on *Father Knows Best.*
2) Who was the star of *Waterfront*?
3) Who was the sometime governor on *Hawaii Five-O*?
4) Name eight major characters on *Howdy Doody.*
5) Name Gomer Pyle's girlfriend.

CHAPTER THIRTY-FOUR

Super-Impossibles!!!!!

If you are one of the lucky few in the running for a Certificate of TV Freakdom, regard these Super-Impossibles as the final elimination round. This is the big one, the trial by fire. If you can get by these questions, you're guaranteed a place of honor in the TV Trivianado Hall of Fame.

Super-Impossibles! ! ! ! !

1) What was the name of Charles Bronson's TV series?
2) Who was the original Riley on TV's *Life of Riley*?
3) Where did Chester A. Riley live (i.e., the street address)?
4) Who was John Russell's sidekick on *Soldiers of Fortune*?
5) Who developed the story line for the *Checkmate* TV series?
6) What was the name of the company used on the old *Price Is Right* that installed the tabulator registering the dollar amount in front of the contestants?
7) Who played Pahoo-ka-ta-wah on *Yancy Derringer*?
8) Name the four actors who portrayed Martin Kane.
9) Who was the very, very first captain of the Starship *Enterprise* and who played him?
10) Who was the star of *The Buccaneers*?
11) What was the Lone Ranger's real name (in the series) before he put on the black mask?
12) What kind of car was used in *My Mother, the Car*?
13) Who was the host of *Strike It Rich*?
14) What role did Maurice Gosfield play in *The Phil Silvers Show (You'll Never Get Rich)*?
15) Sheriff Deadeye, Cauliflower McPugg, and The Mean Widdle Kid were all characterizations in which comedian's repertoire.
16) Who was noted for his portrayal of Sommerset Win-

terset and was also a member of a singing group called "The Haircuts"?

17) Who played Crunch and Des?
18) Who played the Pied Piper of Hamlin?
19) What was Ozzie Nelson's occupation on *Ozzie and Harriet*?

CONCLUSION

"Signing Off . . ."

This concludes Volume I of *The World's Greatest TV Quiz.* By now you realize that all TV husbands are fools, dogs are smarter than people, war can be fun, bad guys have lots of class, and entertaining ghosts in your living room is not entirely out of the ordinary. So the question is raised: does TV create the fads and mores of society, or does it simply mirror what society projects? If, in truth, television reflects reality, then advertising executives marry witches, mothers are reincarnated (re-in*car*nated?) in the form of automobiles, crime apparently never pays, and every trauma in life can be resolved in thirty, sixty, or ninety minutes—depending on how much money the sponsor is willing to sink into the program.

Okay, then. The so-called Golden Age of TV was not without its tarnish. However, on the other hand, there was a sweet simplicity of purpose and emotion about those early years that lingers pleasantly in our minds. It is much too easy to dismiss those founding sitcoms and private eye shows as trash; it is much too easy to mock the heroic good intentions of frontier sheriffs and hard-nosed flatfeet. Rather, we should accept the era as a whole, cautious but fair in our praise and damnation, and perhaps, in the end, simply grateful for our many fond memories of that remarkable age.

ANSWERS

CHAPTER ONE: *"And Your Mission, Should You Decide to Accept It . . ."*

Completion

1) Peter Lawford was Nick Charles; Phyllis Kirk was Nora Charles. (This is a TV quiz, remember?) (1 point each)
2) Gardner McKay. (1 pt.)
3) Jack Lescoulie. (1 pt.)
4) Arlene Francis; Dorothy Kilgallen; Bennett Cerf; and John Charles Daly, host. (The fourth panel member rotated weekly.) (1 pt. each)
5) Princess SummerFallWinterSpring and Chief Thunderthud. (We will accept Chief Thunderchicken.) (1 pt. each)

TOTAL POSSIBLE POINTS: 9

Matching (1 pt. each)

1) c. Richard Boone.
2) a. Gene Barry.
3) d. Jack Lord.
4) b. Will Hutchins.

TOTAL POSSIBLE POINTS: 4

True or False (1 pt. each)

1) False. (Ollie was a dragon. If you're wrong, join the crowd.)
2) False. (This was a detective show based in New Orleans.)
3) True.
4) True. (An offshoot of *Empire,* the show underwent a name change but kept Egan as the star.)
5) False. (Personally, we prefer Brand X.)

TOTAL POSSIBLE POINTS: 5

Multiple Choice (1 pt. each)

1) c. Guy Williams.
2) c. Hal March.
3) a. "Shrimp Boats Are A-Comin'."
4) b. Ginger. (If you put Harriet, remember—this was a family show.)
5) c. Mel Brooks. (He never appeared on the show, but was one of the head writers.)

TOTAL POSSIBLE POINTS: 5

CHAPTER TWO: *"I Love Lucy"*

1) Lucille Ball—Lucy Ricardo.
Desi Arnaz—Ricky Ricardo.
Vivian Vance—Ethel Mertz.
William Frawley—Fred Mertz.
(1 pt. each for a possible 8)
2) McGillicutty. (1 pt.)
3) Ethel Maye Potter. (1 pt.)
4) Jamestown, New York. (1 pt.)
5) Albuquerque, New Mexico. (1 pt.)
6) Band leader at the Tropicana. (1 pt. each)
7) Landlords. (1 pt.)
8) Vaudeville. (1 pt.)
9) Little Ricky. (1 pt.)
10) Mrs. Trumble. (1 pt.)
11) Mickey. (1 pt.)
12) He played the drums. (1 pt.)
13) Bab-a-lu. (1 pt.)
14) Cuba. (1 pt.)
15) East 68th Street. (1 pt.)

TOTAL POSSIBLE POINTS: 23

CHAPTER THREE: *Private Eyes, Dicks, Shamuses, and Flatfeet*

(1 pt. each)

1) g. *Peter Gunn.*
2) f. *Richard Diamond.* (Sam was his attractive switchboard operator who was never seen full-view.)
3) h. *Longstreet.* (Pax was his seeing-eye dog.)
4) i. *The FBI.*
5) e. *Dragnet.* (Ben Alexander was Jack Webb's partner.)
6) l. *77 Sunset Strip.*
7) j. *Hawaiian Eye.*
8) k. *Arrest and Trial.* (Gazzara played the cop; Connors, the lawyer.)
9) o. *Naked City.*
10) m. *Tightrope.*
11) a. *Philip Marlowe.*
12) d. *The Girl from U.N.C.L.E.* (He was Stephanie Powers' partner.)
13) c. *87th Precinct.* (She played Robert Lansing's deaf-mute wife.)
14) n. *Mike Hammer.* (Not to be confused with Mickey Spillane.)
15) e. *Hawaii Five-O.*

TOTAL POSSIBLE POINTS: 15

CHAPTER FOUR: *True and False: A Little Bit of Everything*

(1 pt. each)

1) False. (Gotcha! His name was Fred Finn. Mickey had a better place to put garters.)
2) True. (They were regulars on Uncle Miltie's short-lived 1966 series. It's not for this vehicle that the critics and public refer to him as Mr. Television.)

3) False. (His name was George. Esteban Liberace?? You gotta be kidding . . .)
4) True. (Paul Peterson recorded "My Dad"; Shelley Fabares recorded "Johnny Angel.")
5) True. (In real life, they were married.)
6) True. (Rich Little was the one with all the wild schemes.)
7) False. (He was a corporal. Yeah, we're sneaky. . . . But if you score a 100 percent on this test, that makes you smarter than us.)
8) False. (It was a series called *Noah's Ark* [1956]. It was produced by Jack Webb. Paul Burke was not in *Naked City* until 1960.)
9) False. (He starred in the movie by that name, but produced the TV series. William Reynolds starred in the TV series.)
10) False. (William Shatner starred in *For the People*; Carl Betz starred in *Judd for the Defense*.)
11) True. (Didn't you recognize those legs?)
12) False. (The Invaders each had a crooked little finger.)
13) False. (He was an M.D., but rarely stopped to save anybody.)
14) False. (George Reeves played Superman. Steve Reeves played Hercules.)
15) True. (Lee J. Cobb was the older attorney. Zalman King and Judy Pace were co-stars.)

TOTAL POSSIBLE POINTS: 15

CHAPTER FIVE: *They Clinked and Clanked and Barked and Clawed and Oinked and Galloped Their Way into Our Hearts*

1) Cleo (a basset hound). (1 pt.)
2) Arnold Ziffel. (The first name will do. If you said Ziffel too, you get the "I-Watched-All-170-Episodes-of-*Green Acres*" Award.) (1 pt.)

3) Trigger (Roy's horse).
Bullet (Roy's dog).
Buttermilk (Dale's horse).
Nellie Belle (Pat's jeep). (1 pt. each)
4) Clarence and Judy. (1 pt. each)
5) Topper. (1 pt.)
6) Champion. (1 pt.)
7) Daisy. (1 pt.)
8) Mr. Ed. (If you thought for longer than three seconds, you lose a point. If you didn't get it at all, you lose ten points and the mortgage on your house.) (1 pt.)
9) Julie Newmar. (Her name was Rhoda the Robot.) (1 pt.)
10) Tramp. (1 pt.)
11) Ladadog. (1 pt.)
12) Ruff. (1 pt.)
13) Scout. (1 pt.)
14) Ann Sothern. (1 pt.)
15) Mighty Manfred (The Wonder Dog). (1 pt.)

TOTAL POSSIBLE POINTS: 18

CHAPTER SIX: *They Went on to Bigger and Better Things*

1) Herschel Bernardi. (1 pt.)
2) Carol Burnett. (1 pt.)
3) Jim Backus. (If you can call *Gilligan's Island* bigger and better things.) (1 pt.)
4) Don Knotts, Tom Poston, and Louis Nye. (1 pt. each)
5) Steve McQueen. (1 pt.)
6) Buddy Ebsen. (1 pt.)
7) *Name That Tune.* (1 pt.)
8) Joyce Brothers. (1 pt.)
9) John Cassavetes. (1 pt.)
10) Harvey Lembeck. (They can't all be easy.) (1 pt.)
11) Clint Eastwood (on *Rawhide*). (1 pt.)

12) Cloris Leachman. (Oscar for *The Last Picture Show*; Emmy for *The Mary Tyler Moore Show*.) (1 pt.)
13) Ronald Reagan. (1 pt.)
14) Richard Crenna. (1 pt.)
15) Mike Nichols. (1 pt.)

TOTAL POSSIBLE POINTS: 17

CHAPTER SEVEN: *"Right Here, on Our Stage . . ."*

(1 pt. each)

1) d. Jimmy Durante.
2) d. Jack Linkletter (Art's son).
3) a. *Toast of the Town.*
4) b. Durward Kirby.
5) c. Nancy Ames.
6) c. Cookie Bear.
7) b. Leslie Uggams.
8) b. Steve Lawrence.
9. b. Ray Bolger.
10) a. Julius LaRosa (for a while, anyhow . . .).
11) c. One. (Bob Newhart hosted an hour-long comedy show for which he won an Emmy; the show was subsequently cancelled.)
12) d. CBS.
13) d. David Steinberg.
14) b. Bobby Sherman.
15) c. Perry Como.
16) a. The June Taylor Dancers.
17) c. Foster Brooks. (In real life, Tom Brooks played his brother.)
18) b. "When the Moon Comes Over the Mountain."
19) c. "As the Stomach Turns."
20) c. Colgate.

TOTAL POSSIBLE POINTS: 20

CHAPTER EIGHT: *Perry Mason: He Always Got His Man . . . Off!*

(1 pt. each)

1) Raymond Burr.
2) Barbara Hale.
3) Gertie.
4) Lt. Tragg (not one of your big grinners).
5) Ray Collins.
6) Hamilton Burger. (He, too, was not known for his sparkling personality.)
7) William Talman.
8) Paul Drake.
9) William Hopper (Hedda Hopper's son).
10) Los Angeles.
11) Two.
12) Erle Stanley Gardner.
13) None. (Why else would 271 accused murderers hire him?)
14) 271. (You can't say we never give you a break.)
15) Nine years. (1957 to 1966. Seems longer, doesn't it?)

TOTAL POSSIBLE POINTS: 15

CHAPTER NINE: *Mindbenders #1*

1) Lee Bowman; Hugh Marlowe; George Nader; and Lee Phillips. (1 pt. each)
2) Glenn Corbett. (1 pt.)
3) David Carradine. (Alan Ladd played *Shane* in the film. David Carradine is more popularly known for *Kung Fu*.) (1 pt.)
4) Nancy Kulp. (Don't you notice the resemblance?) (1 pt.)
5) Sebastian Cabot; Doug McClure; and Anthony George. (1 pt. each)

TOTAL POSSIBLE POINTS: 10

CHAPTER TEN: *Sidekicks: They Rode Together*

Part One (1 pt. each)

1) l. Pat Buttram.
2) g. Tonto.
3) o. Andy Devine.
4) a. Burt Ward. (Holy Oleo!)
5) m. Ilya Kuryakin.
6) c. Pat Brady.
7) b. Boo-boo.
8) n. Barney Rubble.
9) k. Pahoo-Ka-Ta-Wah.
10) e. Peter Brown.
11) f. Chester Goode.
12) d. Bob-a-lou.
13) j. Tony Randall. (They played fellow schoolteachers on *Mr. Peepers.*)
14) h. Ethel Mertz.
15) i. Gillis.

TOTAL POSSIBLE POINTS: 15

CHAPTER TEN: *Sidekicks: They Rode Together*

Part Two (1 pt. each)

1) h. Artemus Gordon.
2) f. Kato.
3) k. Maynard G. Krebs.
4) m. Barney Fife.
5) i. Buzz Murdock.
6) b. Buddy Ebsen.
7) o. Mudd (with two *d*'s, played by Sid Melton).
8) n. Rags.
9) c. Sid Melton.
10) d. Bob Denver.
11) j. Cullen Crabbe. (Cullen played Cubby to Buster's Captain Gallant.)

12) g. Norman Fell (on *Dan August*).
13) e. Little John.
14) l. Ruff.
15) a. Rocket J. Squirrel.

TOTAL POSSIBLE POINTS: 15

CHAPTER ELEVEN: *The National Babysitter, or, "Quit Bugging Me and Go Watch TV!"*

(1 pt. each)

1) a. Jay North.
2) c. Bob Keeshan.
3) b. Theodore. (We hope you enjoyed this question as much as we did.)
4) e. Neal Hamilton.
5) e. Phyllis Coates. (Noel Neill was the second Lois Lane. Lana Wood is Natalie's sister. Lana Lang was Superboy's girlfriend in the comics. And Chris Noel was an erstwhile actress and disc jockey, especially popular in Vietnam.)
6) d. Bob Clampett.
7) c. Augie-Doggie. (See comment to answer #3.)
8) b. Jack Barry. (Remember the crayons on the TV screen?)
9) a. Wally Cox. (Lowell Thomas was not a cartoon character.)
10) c. Billie Hayes. (Billie Burke was a Ziegfeld girl: also a very nice witch in *The Wizard of Oz.* Margaret Hamilton was the Wicked Witch of the West in that same movie.)
11) c. Kirby Grant.
12) b. Johnny Weissmuller. (He also played the role in the movies.)
13) c. Richard Crane. (John Glenn was his understudy.)
14) b. Molly Bee.
15) d. Jimmy Dodd.

TOTAL POSSIBLE POINTS: 15

CHAPTER TWELVE: *The Mayberry Saga*

1) Sheriff. (1 pt.)
2) Mayberry, North Carolina. (1 pt. each)
3) Ronnie Howard played Opie Taylor. (1 pt. each)
4) Aunt Bee Taylor, played by Frances Bavier. (1 pt. each)
5) Don Knotts played Barney Fife. (1 pt. each)
6) Gomer Pyle, played by Jim Nabors. (1 pt. each)
7) Goober Pyle, played by George Lindsay. (1 pt. each)
8) Howard Morris (sometimes director). (1 pt.)
9) Otis Campbell, played by Hal Smith. (Not Stubby Kaye. Not that you picked Stubby Kaye, but one of the authors did.) (1 pt. each)
10) Floyd, played by Howard McNeer. (1 pt. each)
11) Helen Crump, played by Aneta Corsaut. (He also dated Elinor Donahue and Joanna Moore, but Aneta Corsaut prevailed. By the way, Aneta was Steve McQueen's co-star in *The Blob*.) (1 pt. each)
12) Teacher. (Elinor ran the drugstore; Joanna Moore was a nurse.) (1 pt.)
13) Thelma Lou, played by Betty Lynn. (What you call your basic townie.) (1 pt. each)
14) The one bullet he was allowed to carry . . . but not in his gun. (1 pt.)
15) Mt. Pilot. (Wrong! Not Mt. Idy.) (1 pt.)
16) Jack Dodson. (1 pt.)
17) Paul Hartman ran the Fix-It Shop. (1 pt. each)
18) Jack Burns (of Burns and Schreiber). (1 pt.)
19) Eight seasons. (1 pt.)
20) Two cells. (1 pt.)

TOTAL POSSIBLE POINTS: 31

CHAPTER THIRTEEN: *The Who, What, Where, How, Why, Name That, and Who Cares Matching Game*

(1 pt. each)

1) h. Groucho Marx.
2) l. Johnny Carson.
3) j. Art Linkletter.
4) b. Jack Bailey.
5) k. Jan Murray.
6) n. Art Fleming.
7) m. Bill Cullen.
8) c. Richard Hayes.
9) e. Bud Collyer.
10) f. Bud Collyer.
11) d. Carl Reiner.
12) o. Allen Ludden.
13) g. Mike Stokey.
14) a. Tom Kennedy.
15) i. Garry Moore.

TOTAL POSSIBLE POINTS: 15

CHAPTER FOURTEEN: *What They Did Besides Live Next Door*

(1 pt. each)

1) a. Dentist. (Have you ever seen a chiropractor on TV?)
2) c. Same as Ozzie's.
3) c. Student. (He may have been all of those mentioned, but officially he was merely a student.)
4) c. Landlord.
5) a. Domestic engineer. (Actually, we made that up. He's a housewife.)
6) b. Gas station attendant. (But we have it on good

authority that he was *studying* to be a brain surgeon.)

7) c. Sewer worker. (See, told you we were nice guys.)
8) a. Department store window dresser.
9) c. Airline pilot. (Wendy and *who*??)
10) a. Factory worker (aircraft).

TOTAL POSSIBLE POINTS: 10

CHAPTER FIFTEEN: "*The Dick Van Dyke Show*"

1) Rob Petrie. (1 pt.)
2) Comedy writer. (1 pt.)
3) Laura Petrie. (1 pt.)
4) Mary Tyler Moore. (Yummy!)
(1 pt.—and a Gold Star if you said "Yummy!")
5) Dancer. (1 pt.)
6) In the Army or the Service.
(1 pt. Sorry, just one point. We will not accept Army *and* Service!)
7) Millie and Jerry Helper. (1 pt. each)
8) Ann Morgan Guillbert and Jerry Paris. (1 pt. each)
9) Richie. (1 pt.)
10) Freddy. (The Program Director at our local CBS affiliate didn't know either, so don't feel bad.) (1 pt.)
11) Buddy Sorel. (1 pt.)
12) Sally Rogers. (1 pt.)
13) Pickles. (1 pt.)
14) Herman Glempshure. (Check with Herman's mother for correct spelling.) (1 pt.)
15) *The Alan Brady Show.* (1 pt.)
16) Carl Reiner (with or without his toupee). (1 pt.)
17) Mel Cooley (aptly named). (1 pt.)
18) Richard Deacon. (1 pt.)
19) Brother-in-law. (Gee, we wonder how he got the job.) (1 pt.)
20) New Rochelle. (1 pt.)

TOTAL POSSIBLE POINTS: 22

CHAPTER SIXTEEN: *Hosts, Voices, and Narrators*

(1 pt. each)

1) William Conrad. (You may know him better as Cannon.)
2) Edward Everett Horton. (He was one of the first actors to claim residuals.)
3) Burr Tillstrom. (Who wasn't bad with his hands, either. . . . Ask Fran.)
4) Walter Winchell. (Acid penned, acid voiced . . .)
5) Jack Webb. (He talked like he acted.)
6) Johnny Olsen.
7) Alistair Cooke. (Not many know he is an American citizen.)
8) Jay Stewart.
9) Cleo the dog.
10) Hugh Downs.
11) Richard Boone.
12) Ed Herlihy. (One of your basic cheese eaters.)
13) Regis Philbin. (And erstwhile host . . .)
14) Truman Bradley.
15) Jim McKay.
16) Michael Anthony or Marvin Miller.
17) Jim Backus.
18) Herschel Bernardi.
19) Tony Marvin (until he was fired by Godfrey).
20) Sam Jaffe. (Besides playing Dr. Zorba, he did the show's famous opening: "Man, Woman, Birth, Death, Infinity. . . .")

TOTAL POSSIBLE POINTS: 20

CHAPTER SEVENTEEN: *Mindbenders #2*

1) Sealtest. (1 pt.)
2) Tom Tryon (later author of *The Other*). (1 pt.)
3) Verna Felton. (Not Frances Rafferty.) (1 pt.)

4) Peggy Wood. (1 pt.)
5) George Fenneman. (He was the announcer; Groucho Marx was the host.) (1 pt.)

TOTAL POSSIBLE POINTS: 5

CHAPTER EIGHTEEN: *The "Who's Who" of Westerns*

1) Jay Silverheels. (1 pt.)
2) Richard Boone. (1 pt.)
3) Rory Calhoun. (1 pt.)
4) John Russell. (1 pt.)
5) Scott Forbes. (Whatever happened to Scott Forbes?) (1 pt.)
6) Will Hutchins. (1 pt.)
7) Darren McGavin. (1 pt.)
8) John Payne. (1 pt.)
9) Clint Eastwood and Eric Fleming. (1 pt. each)
10) Jeffrey Hunter. (1 pt.)
11) Jack Elam and Chad Everett. (1 pt. each)
12) Ty Hardin. (1 pt.)
13) Clint Walker. (1 pt.)
14) John Mills and Sean Garrison. (1 pt. each)
15) John Smith, Robert Fuller, Hoagy Carmichael, and Spring Byington. (1 pt. each)
16) Gail Davis. (1 pt.)
17) Jack Lord. (1 pt.)
18) Duncan Renaldo. (1 pt.)
19) Edgar Buchanan. (1 pt.)
20) Gene Barry. (1 pt.)
21) Peter Breck. (1 pt.)
22) Tommy Nolan. (1 pt.)
23) Rex Allen. (Now he prescribes Chuck Wagon on commercials for Ralston Purina.) (1 pt.)
24) Walter Brennan. (1 pt.)
25) Glenn Ford. (1 pt.)
26) Michael Ansara. (1 pt.)
27) Chris Jones and Allen Case. (1 pt. each)

28) Rex Reason. (Whom else would you expect not to need a gun?) (1 pt.)
29) Johnny Crawford. (*The Naked Ape?*) (1 pt.)
30) Pat Conway and Richard Eastham. (1 pt. each)
31) Ward Bond and John McIntire. (1 pt. each)
32) Robert Culp. (1 pt.)
33) Don Murray and Otis Young. (1 pt. each)
34) Phillip Carey, Neville Brand, Peter Brown, and William Smith (not necessarily in that order). (1 pt. each)
35) Dale Robertson. (1 pt.)

TOTAL POSSIBLE POINTS: 48

CHAPTER NINETEEN: *Nemeses, Foils, and Bad Guys*

Part One (1 pt. each)

1) f. The Robinson family.
2) h. James West.
3) l. Dudley Do-Right.
4) k. Tom Terrific.
5) j. Howdy Doody.
6) m. U.N.C.L.E.
7) c. Steve McGarrett.
8) n. Batman.
9) g. Bullwinkle.
10) e. Herbert Philbrick.
11) i. Colonel Hogan.
12) a. Phil Silvers.
13) o. Elliot Ness.
14) b. Darren Stevens (or Darrel, Denton, Danton, etc., etc. . . .).
15) d. Wiley Coyote.

TOTAL POSSIBLE POINTS: 15

CHAPTER NINETEEN: *Nemeses, Foils, and Bad Guys*

Part Two (1 pt. each)

1) d. The Federation. (Think!)
2) g. *The Fugitive.*
3) j. McHale.
4) m. Mr. Wilson.
5) k. Jerry Van Dyke (on *My Mother, the Car*).
6) l. CONTROL.
7) n. F Troop.
8) b. Perry Mason.
9) e. Gomer Pyle.
10) f. Oliver Douglas.
11) i. The Clampetts.
12) o. Jason Bolt.
13) c. Danny Williams (Danny Thomas's name on the show).
14) h. Zorro.
15) a. King Leonardo.

TOTAL POSSIBLE POINTS: 15

CHAPTER TWENTY: *"Whaddaya Mean, War Is Hell?"*

(1 pt. each)

1) c. Paul Ford.
2) f. Jimmy Boyd. (The aforementioned women were co-stars in this short-lived series about a man named Marion who was drafted into the WAVES.)
3) d. Sammy Jackson. (Andy Griffith starred in the movie and the play; Jim Nabors was his protege.)
4) d. PT-73.
5) e. Denny Miller. (They all played "husbands," but you had to be 6'3" to portray Juliet's mate.)
6) d. Dean Jones.

7) b. Tom D'Andrea and Hal March. (You're probably wondering how we came up with answer "e." Well it happened like this . . .
Bornhauser: "Don't you see? Jean Seberg and Ingrid Bergman both played Joan of Arc, see? Soldiers. . . .
Palumbo: Gosh, we're clever!)
8) d. Illinois. (His "I" letter sweater did not stand for "idiot," obviously.)
9) b. Roger Smith.
10) b. Bill Daily. (Nice guess.)
11) e. Dentist (and part-time philosopher).
12) e. Abby Dalton (and part-time "Yummy").
13) c. Robert.
14) b. Jack Warden. (Gary Collins was the ranking Navy officer. Rick Nelson was in the movie. Joe Flynn was in *McHale's Navy*. Monte Markham was the second Perry Mason . . . and he weren't never in the Navy!)
15) d. Stalag 13.
16) a. Fort Courage.
17) d. Quentin.
18) c. "Shazam!" (The magic word that changed humble newsboy Billy Batson into crime-busting Captain Marvel . . . with the aid of a benevolent lightning bolt from the heavens.)
19) d. Radar.
20) b. Camp Henderson.

TOTAL POSSIBLE POINTS: 20

CHAPTER TWENTY-ONE: *"Topper"*

1) Leo G. Carroll. (1 pt.)
2) Lee Patrick. (1 pt.)
3) They were ghosts. (We'll accept "They were dead" as an answer, but we think you're morbid.) (1 pt.)
4) It was their house. Topper bought it after they died. (1 pt.)

5) George and Marion Kirby. (1 pt. each)
6) Robert Sterling and Anne Jeffreys. (1 pt. each)
7) St. Bernard. (1 pt.)
8) Neil. (1 pt.)
9) He was an alcoholic. ("Drunk" will do.) (1 pt.)
10) They were killed in an avalanche. (1 pt.)

TOTAL POSSIBLE POINTS: 12

CHAPTER TWENTY-TWO: *You Remember Them for This . . .*

(1 pt. each)

1) True.
2) False. (Badge 714.)
3) False. (Juliet Mills starred. She's Hayley's sister.)
4) True.
5) True.
6) True.
7) False. (He was a court-martialed officer and a drifter.)
8) True. (*McHale's Navy* and *The Tim Conway Show*.)
9) True.
10) False. (He played Bat Masterson.)
11) True.
12) False. (It was Paula Prentiss, not Ann. Ann appeared with William Daniels and Alice Ghostley in *Captain Nice*.)
13) True.
14) True. (He's the only perpetual beachboy in the world. We can't knock it—at least he gets work.)
15) True.
16) True. (He played a writer on *Window on Main Street*. And if you don't know what he did in the other two shows, forget it.)
17) False. (You never saw Gladys on *December Bride*.)
18) True. (Kit Carson was played by Bill Williams . . .

who was married to Barbara Hale, who played Della Street.)

19) False. (It was Robert Horton.)

20) True. (And you thought *Cosmopolitan* discovered him!)

21) False. (Sammy Spear was Jackie Gleason's bandleader. Bob Hope's is Les Brown and his Band of Renown.)

22) True. (Don Porter played her boss in *Private Secretary* and in *The Ann Sothern Show.* Ernest Truex played her boss for thirteen segments of *The Ann Sothern Show.*)

23) False. (Ann B. Davis was not in Bob Cummings' second show.)

24) False. (At one time, *Batman* appeared twice weekly on ABC.)

25) False. (Herbert Philbrick was the character's name; Richard Carlson portrayed him.)

TOTAL POSSIBLE POINTS: 25

CHAPTER TWENTY-THREE: *"The Butler Did It"*

1) Alfred Pennyworth, played by Alan Napier. (1 pt. each)
2) Shirley Booth. (If we said Hazel, that would have been too easy.) (1 pt.)
3) Mr. French, played by Sebastian Cabot. (1 pt. each)
4) Kato, played by the late Kung Fu film star Bruce Lee. (1 pt. each)
5) Hop Sing. (1 pt.)
6) Mrs. Livingston. (1 pt.)
7) Juliet Mills. (1 pt.)
8) Manners. (1 pt.)
9) Silas. (1 pt.)
10) Ann B. Davis (also known as Schultzy). (1 pt.)
11) Nancy Walker played Mildred. (1 pt. each)
12) Grindl. (1 pt.)

13) Rockwell Sin, played by Jack Soo. (1 pt. each)
14) Larry Hagman and Donna Mills. (They gave up the hectic life for the good life. It may have been good, but it was short; the show died in thirteen weeks.) (1 pt. each)
15) Arthur Treacher. (Would you want to be Merv Griffin's butler?) (1 pt.)

TOTAL POSSIBLE POINTS: 21

CHAPTER TWENTY-FOUR: *"Answers, We've Got Answers . . ."*

1) b. Harry Morgan and Cara Williams. (1 pt.)
2) d. Ronny Burns. (1 pt.)
3) c. June Blair. (1 pt.)
4) b. Tommy Rettig. (Here's the rundown: Tommy Rettig was the first owner, Jon Provost was the second. Elizabeth Taylor was the owner in the movie, for all you World War II freaks. Jay North played Dennis the Menace. And Mickey Dolenz was a "Monkee.") (1 pt.)
5) a. Ed Begley, b. Lorne Greene (1 pt.)
6) c. Robert Taylor. (1 pt.)
7) d. Burgess Meredith. (We thought that was pretty hard, too.) (1 pt.)
8) d. Fred Astaire. (All the people listed, however, were hosts of series.) (1 pt.)
9) a. James Whitmore. (1 pt.)
10) b. Wilbur Post. (1 pt.)
11) a. Marjorie Lord. (1 pt.)
12) b. Jim Davis. (1 pt.)
13) d. Nita Talbot. (Lovely Nita. . . .) (1 pt.)
14) c. Red Buttons. (1 pt.)
15) d. Mrs. Calabash. (1 pt.)
16) a. Robert Goulet. (He had the same luck with espionage as he had with "The Star-Spangled Banner.") (1 pt.)
17) b. *The Monroes.* (1 pt.)

18) c. Dick Powell. (1 pt.)
19) d. Ron Ely. (All the others played Tarzan in the movies, except J. Fred Muggs . . . who played Tarzan on radio.) (1 pt.)
20) d. Jed had discovered oil. (All the others would have been better ideas, but consider the source.) (1 pt.)

TOTAL POSSIBLE POINTS: 20

CHAPTER TWENTY-FIVE: *Mindbenders #3*

1) Garry Moore, host; Bill Cullen, Bess Myerson, Henry Morgan, and Betsy Palmer (not necessarily in that order). (1 pt. each)
2) Jock Mahoney. (1 pt.)
3) Josh Randall. (Sounds like a bounty hunter, doesn't it? Can you imagine Percival Wentwhistle?) (1 pt. each)
4) Bobby Buntrock. (1 pt.)
5) Earl Holliman. (What can you say about Earl Holliman?) (1 pt.)

TOTAL POSSIBLE POINTS: 9

CHAPTER TWENTY-SIX: *"Gunsmoke"*

1) James Arness. (1 pt.)
2) Amanda Blake. (1 pt.)
3) Russell. (1 pt.)
4) The Longbranch. (1 pt.)
5) Dodge City, Kansas. (You must include the state.) (1 pt.)
6) Milburn Stone. (1 pt.)
7) Adams. (1 pt.)
8) Dennis Weaver. (1 pt.)
9) Goode. (1 pt.)
10) Festus. (1 pt.)
11) Ken Curtis. (1 pt.)
12) Hagen. (1 pt.)

13) Burt Reynolds. (1 pt.)
14) Glenn Strange. (1 pt.)
15) 1955. (1 pt.)

TOTAL POSSIBLE POINTS: 15

CHAPTER TWENTY-SEVEN: *"Why Not?"*

(1 pt. each)

1) True. (Captain Binghamton.)
2) True. (Lassie portrayed a female; Lassie is a male collie.)
3) True.
4) False. (Stuart Whitman starred in *Cimarron Strip*; George Montgomery starred in *Cimarron City*.)
5) False. (On *Have Gun, Will Travel,* one wired Paladin in San Francisco.)
6) False. (Henry Fonda was the sheriff; Alan Case was the deputy.)
7) True. (Lee Meriwether played Catwoman, as well as Julie Newmar and Eartha Kitt. In the feature film, Lee played it.)
8) False. (Mr. Lucky's casino was off the coast of Florida.)
9) False. (Ken Curtis was co-star of *Ripcord*.)
10) False. (Dwayne, Darryl's brother, played Dobie Gillis.)
11) False. (Zasu Pitts was co-star of Gale Storm's second series, *Oh, Susanna,* or, *The Gale Storm Show*.)
12) True.
13) True. (She was portrayed by Gena Rowlands.)
14) False. (Flubadub *was* a duck-billed platypus, but he was also a combination of several other animals.)
15) True. (Tom Tully was his co-star.)

TOTAL POSSIBLE POINTS: 15

CHAPTER TWENTY-EIGHT: "*. . . We've Got Lots and Lots of Answers!*"

(1 pt. each)

1) b. Lloyd Bridges.
2) c. *Judd for the Defense.*
3) d. *The Defenders.* (He was a doctor in *The Bold Ones.*)
4) d. Roger Perry.
5) d. Peter Breck.
6) c. *87th Precinct.*
7) c. Judy Carne.
8) d. Noreen Corcoran. (If you said "c" you automatically get a free year's subscription to the *L.A. Free Press.*)
9) b. The Sons of the Pioneers. (If you answered "e" you're either weird or the world's last remaining beatnik.)
10) a. Raymond Bailey.

TOTAL POSSIBLE POINTS: 10

CHAPTER TWENTY-NINE: "*Star Trek*"

1) Gene Roddenberry. (1 pt.)
2) William Shatner. (1 pt.)
3) Leonard Nimoy. (1 pt.)
4) Vulcan. (1 pt.)
5) DeForest Kelly. (1 pt.)
6) Bones. (1 pt.)
7) Christine Chapel. (1 pt.)
8) Majel Barrett. (1 pt.)
9) Sulu. (1 pt.)
10) George Takei. (1 pt.)
11) Montgomery Scott. (Nickname, Scotty. "*Aye, Captain!!*") (1 pt.)
12) James Doohan. (1 pt.)

13) Lieutenant Uhura. (1 pt.)
14) Nichelle Nichols. (1 pt.)
15) Star Fleet Command. (1 pt.)
16) Do not violate alien cultures. (1 pt.)
17) The Federation. (1 pt.)
18) Klingons. (We will also accept Romulans.) (1 pt.)
19) The "Spock pinch" or "Vulcan pinch." (1 pt.)
20) Phasers (stun or kill). (1 pt.)
21) By a transporter device or teleporter. (1 pt.)
22) Serak and Amanda. (1 pt. each)
23) Jane Wyatt. (1 pt.)
24) The shuttle. (1 pt.)
25) The *Enterprise,* or *United Starship Enterprise.* (1 pt.)

Groove on, trekkies!

TOTAL POSSIBLE POINTS: 26

CHAPTER THIRTY: *"The Play's The Thing"—and It Was Live*

(1 pt. each)

1) Jose Ferrer.
2) Rod Steiger. (Steiger played Marty on TV; Ernest Borgnine later played the role in the film, for which he won an Academy Award.)
3) Jack Palance. (In the film, the boxer was played by Anthony Quinn.)
4) James Dean. (Back in the Fifties all the big talent wanted to be in television.)
5) John F. Kennedy.
6) George Roy Hill (who later directed both *Butch Cassidy and the Sundance Kid* and *The Sting*).
7) Tommy Sands. (The name of the song was "Teenage Crush." Can you sing the lyrics to it? Don't feel bad —neither could Tommy Sands.)
8) Andy Griffith. (Sammy Jackson played the role when it was made into a continuing series.)
9) John Conte.

10) Humphrey Bogart (a re-creation of the role he played in the movie of the same name).
11) Royal Dano.
12) They were all in the cast of *Eloise* on *Playhouse 90.* (And such a weird cast has not been assembled under one roof since *Hellzapoppin.*)
13) All were original TV plays that went on to become feature films.
14) Larry Blyden (an extremely underrated actor).
15) Originally feature films, these were later produced as TV specials.

TOTAL POSSIBLE POINTS: 15

CHAPTER THIRTY-ONE: *"Goodnight, David . . . Goodnight, Chet . . ."*

(1 pt. each)

1) Edward R. Murrow.
2) Walter Cronkite.
3) Charles Kuralt.
4) Walter Winchell. (Though he was mainly known for his work on radio, he did have a TV program.)
5) Douglas Edwards (the first TV news personality!).
6) John Cameron Swayze. (Tick . . . tick . . . tick . . .)
7) Lawrence Spivak. (We have it on good authority that he used to do the audience warm-up for *The Milton Berle Show.*)
8) Dave Garroway.
9) John Cameron Swayze. (Tick . . . tick . . . tick . . . Yes, it's still ticking.)
10) Ted Baxter. (With Ted, you can't be sure he'll close his newscast the same way twice.)

TOTAL POSSIBLE POINTS: 10

CHAPTER THIRTY-TWO: *"Filling In for Johnny Tonight . . ."*

(1 pt. each)

1) Les Crane (former disc jockey and erstwhile actor).
2) Skitch Henderson.
3) Steve Allen.
4) Jack Paar.
5) Genevieve.
6) David Frost (for whom everything was simply "Fantastic!").
7) Merv Griffin.
8) Dick Cavett.
9) Mike Douglas.
10) Dinah Shore. (Gosh, we're clever!)
11) Molly Bee.
12) Arlene Francis.
13) Durward Kirby.
14) Jerry Lewis.
15) Mrs. Miller.

TOTAL POSSIBLE POINTS: 15

CHAPTER THIRTY-THREE: *Mindbenders #4*

1) Betty ("Princess")—Elinor Donahue.
   Bud—Billy Gray.
   Kathy ("Kitten")—Laurin Chapin.
   (1 pt. each for a total of 6)
2) Preston Foster. (1 pt.)
3) Richard Denning. (1 pt.)
4) Howdy Doody, Buffalo Bob Smith, Flubadub, Princess SummerFallWinterSpring, Dilly Dally, Chief Thunderthud, Phineas T. Bluster, Clarabelle, Corny Cobb, Chief Thunderchicken, and John J. Fedoozle, Private Eye.
   (1 pt. each for a total of 8.)

5) Lou Ann Poovie. (1 pt.)

TOTAL POSSIBLE POINTS: 17

CHAPTER THIRTY-FOUR: *Super-Impossibles!!!!!*

1) *Man with a camera.* (2 pts.)
2) Jackie Gleason. (William Bendix played the role later.) (2 pts.)
3) 1313 Blueview Terrace. (2 pts.)
4) Chick Chandler. (2 pts.)
5) Eric Ambler. (2 pts.)
6) American Totalizator Company. (2 pts.)
7) X. Brands. (2 pts.)
8) William Gargan, Lee Tracy, Lloyd Nolan, and Mark Stevens. (2 pts. each)
9) James Pike, played by Jeff Hunter. (2 pts. each)
10) Robert Shaw. (2 pts.)
11) Ranger Dan Reid. (2 pts.)
12) A 1928 Porter. (2 pts.)
13) Warren Hull. (2 pts.)
14) Private Doberman. (2 pts.)
15) Red Skelton. (Klem Kadiddlehopper would've been too easy.) (2 pts.)
16) Sid Caesar. (2 pts.)
17) Forrest Tucker and Sandy Kenyon. (2 pts. each)
18) Van Johnson. (2 pts.)
19) None. (This is a fact. According to Ozzie Nelson himself, the character was supposedly in advertising, but the details of his job were never stipulated on the show.) (2 pts.)

TOTAL POSSIBLE POINTS: 48

If you made it through this section . . . CONGRATULATIONS!

GRAND TOTAL: 660

10-74